# Name the Insects

Write the correct name neatly in the space below each in:
Colour each insect to make a small picture.
Here are the names of the insects to help you.
They are not in the right order.

**ladybird**  **beetle**  **ant**  **bluebottle**  **dragon-fly**  **bee**

**butterfly**  **daddy-long-legs (crane-fly)**  **grasshopper**

**wasp**  **mosquito**  **moth**

1
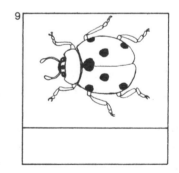

2
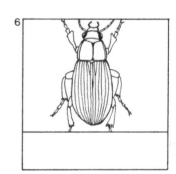

3
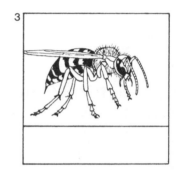

4
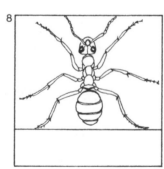

5
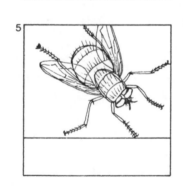

6
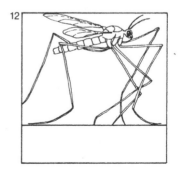

7
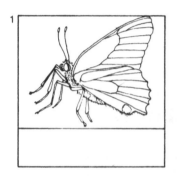

8
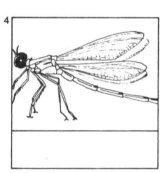

9
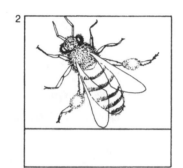

10
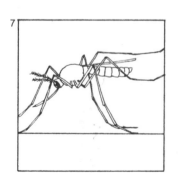

11
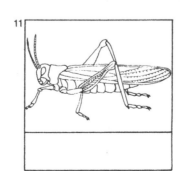

12
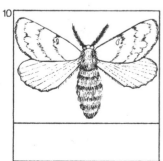

1

# Factors

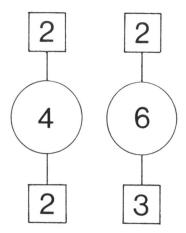

Look at the first of these two drawings.
It shows **2** in the top box and **2** in the bottom box.
**2 × 2 = 4**, so **4** goes in the circle for the answer.

Look at the second of these drawings.
It shows **2** in the top box and **3** in the bottom box.
**2 × 3 = 6** and **3 × 2 = 6**, so **6** is the answer, and goes in the circle.

Now try these. Put the correct answer in each circle.
Make sure the answer works both ways: down (2 × 4) and up (4 × 2).

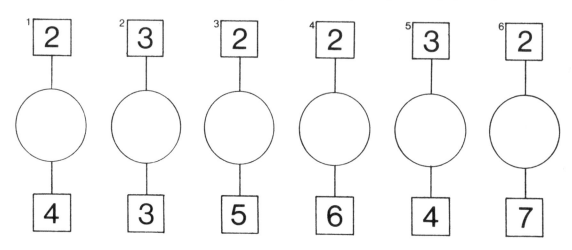

Here are some more for you to try.
Make sure the answers work both ways: down (3 × 5) and up (5 × 3).

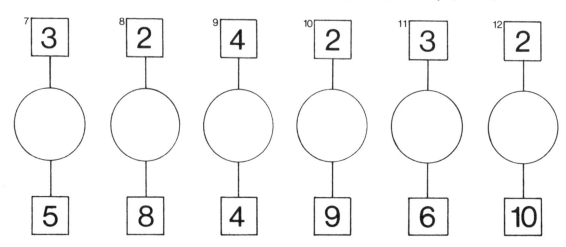

2

# Similar Words

In the space by each word write another word which means the same or nearly the same. Try to do each one by yourself.
If you cannot remember a similar word, you will find one in the jumbled list at the bottom of the page. The first one has been done for you.

| | Word | Similar word | | | Word | Similar word |
|---|---|---|---|---|---|---|
| 1. | **afraid** | **frightened** | | 16. | answer | ................... |
| 2. | ask | ................... | | 17. | bad | ................... |
| 3. | beautiful | ................... | | 18. | begin | ................... |
| 4. | break | ................... | | 19. | city | ................... |
| 5. | close | ................... | | 20. | dish | ................... |
| 6. | dress | ................... | | 21. | end | ................... |
| 7. | fall | ................... | | 22. | fast | ................... |
| 8. | feed | ................... | | 23. | great | ................... |
| 9. | hear | ................... | | 24. | hurt | ................... |
| 10. | look | ................... | | 25. | picture | ................... |
| 11. | present | ................... | | 26. | ship | ................... |
| 12. | sick | ................... | | 27. | stop | ................... |
| 13. | tired | ................... | | 28. | under | ................... |
| 14. | wait | ................... | | 29. | wood | ................... |
| 15. | bag | ................... | | 30. | beat | ................... |

town          damage          boat          lovely          sack          drop

**frightened**          quick          ill          naughty          large          shut

timber          drawing          weary          reply          beg          eat

listen          hit          stay          start          smash          plate

frock          halt          see          finish          gift          beneath

3

# Missing Numbers

Put the missing numbers in the squares.

1. $11 - \boxed{\phantom{0}} = 4$

2. $14 - \boxed{\phantom{0}} = 8$

3. $12 - \boxed{\phantom{0}} = 5$

4. $15 - \boxed{\phantom{0}} = 7$

5. $13 - \boxed{\phantom{0}} = 9$

6. $16 - \boxed{\phantom{0}} = 7$

7. $11 - \boxed{\phantom{0}} = 6$

8. $17 - \boxed{\phantom{0}} = 9$

9. $13 - \boxed{\phantom{0}} = 7$

10. $14 - \boxed{\phantom{0}} = 5$

11. $12 - \boxed{\phantom{0}} = 6$

12. $16 - \boxed{\phantom{0}} = 9$

13. $15 - \boxed{\phantom{0}} = 8$

14. $17 - \boxed{\phantom{0}} = 6$

15. $\boxed{\phantom{0}} - 7 = 5$

16. $\boxed{\phantom{0}} - 9 = 7$

17. $\boxed{\phantom{0}} - 4 = 9$

18. $\boxed{\phantom{0}} - 7 = 4$

19. $\boxed{\phantom{0}} - 8 = 7$

20. $\boxed{\phantom{0}} - 6 = 8$

21. $\boxed{\phantom{0}} - 8 = 9$

22. $\boxed{\phantom{0}} - 5 = 6$

23. $\boxed{\phantom{0}} - 9 = 5$

24. $\boxed{\phantom{0}} - 7 = 8$

25. $\boxed{\phantom{0}} - 6 = 6$

26. $\boxed{\phantom{0}} - 7 = 9$

27. $\boxed{\phantom{0}} - 11 = 6$

28. $\boxed{\phantom{0}} - 6 = 7$

# Alphabetical Order

Put the words in each box into alphabetical order.
Look at the first letter in each word. This usually tells you
where the word must go in alphabetical order. But if the
first letters of two words are the same, you must look at the
second letters, or even the third letters, to find out the order.
The first one has been started for you.
Here is the alphabet to help you.

a  b  c  d  e  f  g  h  i  j  k  l  m  n  o  p  q  r  s  t  u  v  w  x  y  z

**1**

| | |
|---|---|
| boat | **across** |
| **across** | |
| dinner | |
| clean | |

**2**

| | |
|---|---|
| fight | |
| eight | |
| grow | |
| hedge | |

**3**

| | |
|---|---|
| interesting | |
| knew | |
| jumped | |
| leave | |

**4**

| | |
|---|---|
| postman | |
| naughty | |
| minute | |
| outside | |

**5**

| | |
|---|---|
| television | |
| Saturday | |
| quite | |
| rabbit | |

**6**

| | |
|---|---|
| visit | |
| young | |
| walk | |
| use | |

**7**

| | |
|---|---|
| tomorrow | |
| puppy | |
| pretty | |
| Thursday | |

**8**

| | |
|---|---|
| sometimes | |
| nothing | |
| should | |
| nearly | |

5

# Showing the Time

Draw the hands on each clock to show the time.
Remember to make the minute-hand **longer** than the hour-hand.
The first one has been done for you.

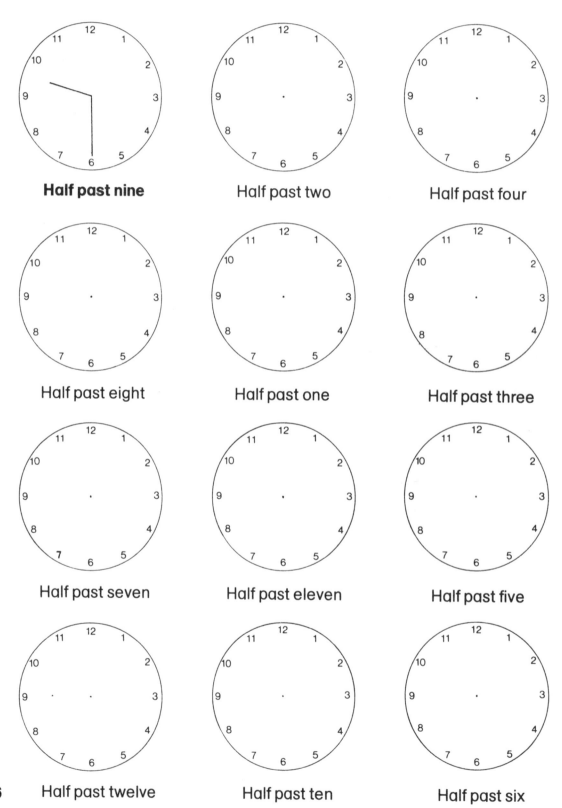

| | | |
|---|---|---|
| **Half past nine** | Half past two | Half past four |
| Half past eight | Half past one | Half past three |
| Half past seven | Half past eleven | Half past five |
| Half past twelve | Half past ten | Half past six |

# Odd Man Out

Colour the one in each row which is different from the others in that row.

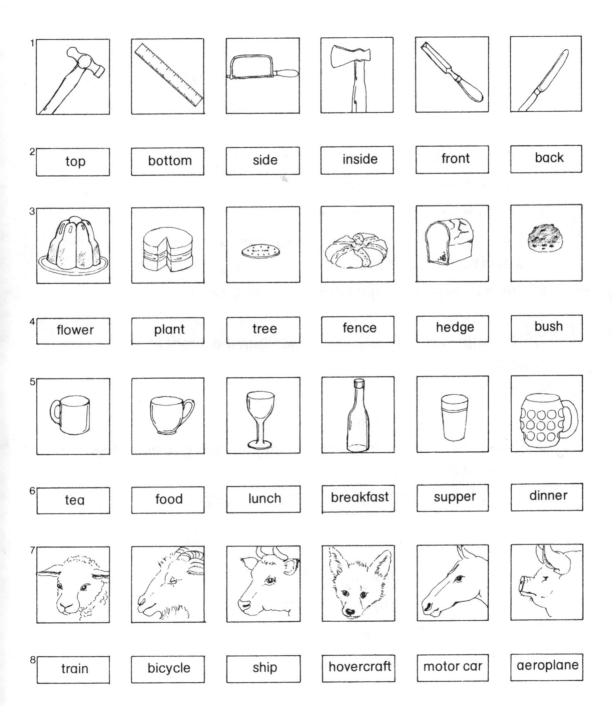

2. | top | bottom | side | inside | front | back |

4. | flower | plant | tree | fence | hedge | bush |

6. | tea | food | lunch | breakfast | supper | dinner |

8. | train | bicycle | ship | hovercraft | motor car | aeroplane |

# Measuring Sticks

Four sticks are drawn on this page.
Colour them like this:

**A Green**
**B Blue**
**C Yellow**
**D Red**

Measure the sticks and complete the sentences below.

1. The red stick is ........cm long.

2. The green stick is ........cm long.

3. The yellow stick is ........cm long.

4. The blue stick is ........cm long.

5. The shortest and the longest sticks together
would be ........cm long.

6. The difference in length between sticks C and D
is ........cm.

7. The longest stick is ........cm longer than the shortest
stick.

8. Stick C is ........cm shorter than stick A.

9. Stick D is twice the length of stick .........

10. You would need three sticks the length of stick B to equal the
length of stick .........

11. Stick A equals the lengths of sticks ........ and ........
together.

12. Stick ........ is 11cm shorter than stick .........

13. Stick B is one-half the length of stick .........

14. Stick B is one-third the length of stick .........

15. Stick ........ is 15cm longer than stick .........

B

C

A

D

# Crosswords

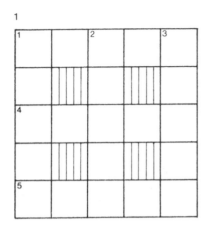

**1**

### Across
1. Has a red breast.
4. Sheep eat this.
5. This day.

### Down
1. Correct.
2. A piece of wood.
3. Not nice.

**2**

### Across
1. Cold part of the year.
4. Used for making hair tidy.
6. A long way down.
7. The one who wins.

### Down
1. This lets the light and air in.
2. Pleasant.
3. For rubbing out.
5. Not shut.

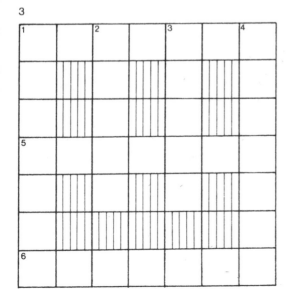

**3**

### Across
1. In charge of the class.
5. Feeling happy.
6. Just before night time.

### Down
1. Baby frog.
2. What they did with the question.
3. Most people live in one.
4. What you are doing with these words.

# Mapping

Map the white circles to the shaded circles by joining pairs whose numbers add to **13**.
Use a purple pencil.

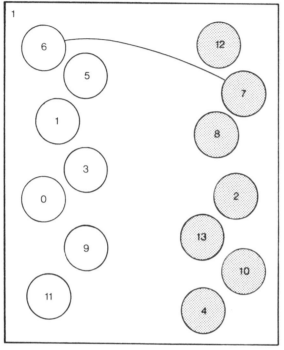

Map the white circles to the shaded circles by joining pairs whose numbers add to **14**.
Use a green pencil.

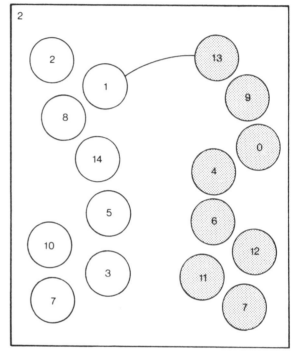

Map the white circles to the shaded circles by joining pairs whose numbers add to **15**.
Use a blue pencil.

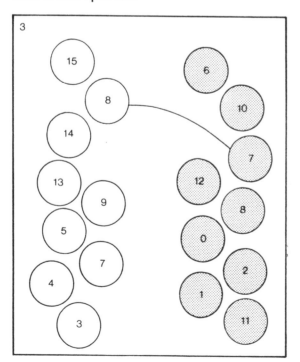

Map the white circles to the shaded circles by joining pairs whose numbers add to **16**.
Use a red pencil.

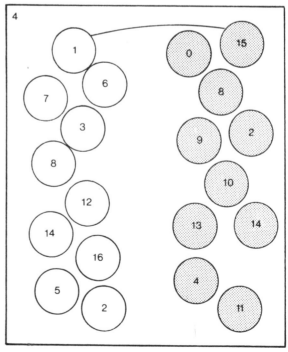

**10**  The first one has been done for you in each case.

# Using Your Dictionary

Find these words in your dictionary and write out their meanings.
Write full sentences.

1.  answer .........................................................................................................
2.  building .......................................................................................................
3.  country .......................................................................................................
4.  different ......................................................................................................
5.  excuse .........................................................................................................
6.  family .........................................................................................................
7.  guess ..........................................................................................................
8.  hope ...........................................................................................................
9.  iron ...........................................................................................................
10. juicy ..........................................................................................................
11. kennel .........................................................................................................
12. lunch ..........................................................................................................
13. minute .........................................................................................................
14. nearly .........................................................................................................
15. ocean ..........................................................................................................
16. present ........................................................................................................
17. quickly ........................................................................................................
18. river ..........................................................................................................
19. second ........................................................................................................
20. try ............................................................................................................
21. under ..........................................................................................................
22. vegetable ......................................................................................................
23. wind ...........................................................................................................
24. year ...........................................................................................................
25. zebra .........................................................................................................

# Operating Numbers

Do what it says to the numbers in the circles.
Put your answers in the squares.

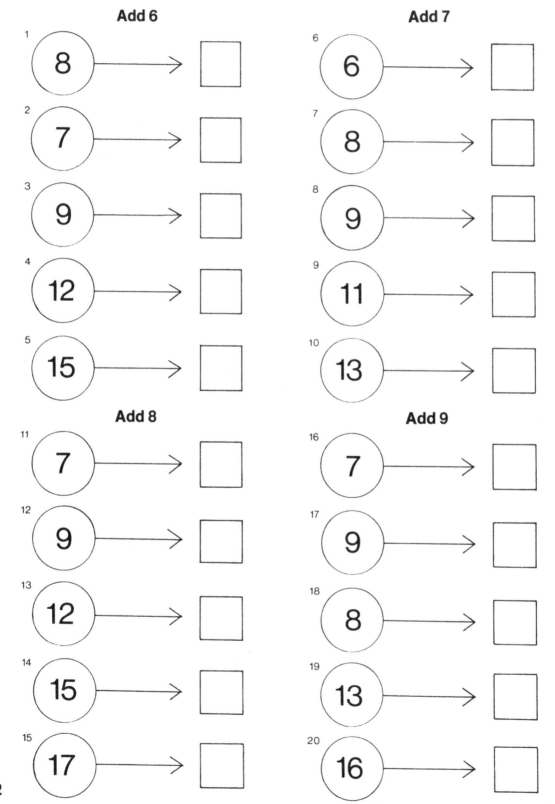

**Add 6**

1. 8 →
2. 7 →
3. 9 →
4. 12 →
5. 15 →

**Add 7**

6. 6 →
7. 8 →
8. 9 →
9. 11 →
10. 13 →

**Add 8**

11. 7 →
12. 9 →
13. 12 →
14. 15 →
15. 17 →

**Add 9**

16. 7 →
17. 9 →
18. 8 →
19. 13 →
20. 16 →

# Change a Wasp into a Dish!

Start with                         **wasp**
Change one of the letters     **wash**
Change another letter         **wish**
Change another letter         **dish**

Here is another one. Change **clap** into **ship**:

Start with                         **clap**
Change one of the letters     **clip**
Change another letter         **slip**
Change another letter         **ship**

Now try these. Can you find two middle words
which change the first word into the last word?

| 1 | 2 | 3 | 4 |
|---|---|---|---|
| read | pass | hide | land |
| | | | |
| | | | |
| lent | most | wish | sent |

| 5 | 6 | 7 | 8 |
|---|---|---|---|
| bent | shoe | feel | cake |
| | | | |
| | | | |
| mind | step | meat | line |

| 9 | 10 | 11 | 12 |
|---|---|---|---|
| pair | talk | care | sand |
| | | | |
| | | | |
| land | well | fine | lead |

13

# Fractions

What fraction of each shape is the shaded part?
Write the fraction at the side of each shape.
The first three have been done for you.

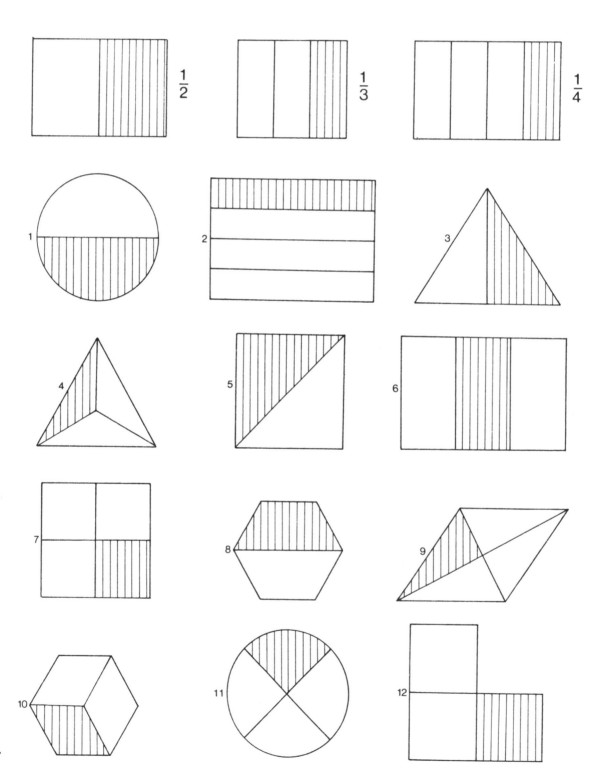

# Opposites

In the space by each word write a word which means the **opposite**.
Try to do each one by yourself. If you cannot remember an opposite,
you will find one in the jumbled list at the bottom of the page.

| | Word | Opposite | | Word | Opposite |
|---|---|---|---|---|---|
| 1. | **bad** | **good** | 16. | hard | ................... |
| 2. | ugly | ................... | 17. | high | ................... |
| 3. | buy | ................... | 18. | hot | ................... |
| 4. | clean | ................... | 19. | kind | ................... |
| 5. | closed | ................... | 20. | hide | ................... |
| 6. | dark | ................... | 21. | asleep | ................... |
| 7. | die | ................... | 22. | stop | ................... |
| 8. | late | ................... | 23. | top | ................... |
| 9. | ever | ................... | 24. | under | ................... |
| 10. | fast | ................... | 25. | warm | ................... |
| 11. | fat | ................... | 26. | windy | ................... |
| 12. | floor | ................... | 27. | young | ................... |
| 13. | great | ................... | 28. | yesterday | ................... |
| 14. | first | ................... | 29. | work | ................... |
| 15. | hit | ................... | 30. | winter | ................... |

| | | | | | |
|---|---|---|---|---|---|
| never | dirty | live | seek | cruel | miss |
| **good** | small | over | low | sell | early |
| calm | summer | start | open | last | awake |
| soft | tomorrow | slow | ceiling | beautiful | |
| old | light | thin | play | cold | cool | bottom |

15

# The Magic Multiplication Square

|     | 1 | 2 | 3 | 4 | 5 | 6 | 7 | 8 | 9 |
|-----|---|---|---|---|---|---|---|---|---|
| x1  | 1 | 2 | 3 | 4 | 5 | 6 | 7 | 8 | 9 |
| x2  | 2 | 4 | 6 | 8 | 10 | 12 | 14 | 16 | 18 |
| x3  | 3 | 6 | 9 | 12 | 15 | 18 | 21 | 24 | 27 |
| x4  | 4 | 8 | 12 | 16 | 20 | 24 | 28 | 32 | 36 |
| x5  | 5 | 10 | 15 | 20 | 25 | 30 | 35 | 40 | 45 |
| x6  | 6 | 12 | 18 | 24 | 30 | 36 | 42 | 48 | 54 |
| x7  | 7 | 14 | 21 | 28 | 35 | 42 | 49 | 56 | 63 |
| x8  | 8 | 16 | 24 | 32 | 40 | 48 | 56 | 64 | 72 |
| x9  | 9 | 18 | 27 | 36 | 45 | 54 | 63 | 72 | 81 |

If you want to use it to work out $7 \times 6$:
Put your finger on **7** in the top line.
Move your finger downwards until it is opposite **6** at the side.
Your finger will then be pointing to the answer, which is **42**.

Now try these, using the **magic multiplication square**.

1.  $2 \times 6 =$ .......
2.  $7 \times 2 =$ .......
3.  $3 \times 7 =$ .......
4.  $8 \times 3 =$ .......
5.  $4 \times 8 =$ .......
6.  $7 \times 8 =$ .......
7.  $9 \times 6 =$ .......
8.  $3 \times 7 =$ .......
9.  $6 \times 8 =$ .......
10. $2 \times 9 =$ .......
11. $3 \times 8 =$ .......
12. $8 \times 7 =$ .......
13. $3 \times 5 =$ .......
14. $6 \times 3 =$ .......
15. $7 \times 4 =$ .......
16. $9 \times 2 =$ .......

17. $9 \times 4 =$ .......
18. $5 \times 9 =$ .......
19. $9 \times 9 =$ .......
20. $4 \times 9 =$ .......
21. $8 \times 2 =$ .......
22. $8 \times 4 =$ .......
23. $7 \times 6 =$ .......
24. $8 \times 9 =$ .......
25. $6 \times 4 =$ .......
26. $5 \times 6 =$ .......
27. $2 \times 8 =$ .......
28. $6 \times 7 =$ .......
29. $7 \times 7 =$ .......
30. $8 \times 6 =$ .......
31. $7 \times 9 =$ .......
32. $5 \times 8 =$ .......

33. $9 \times 3 =$ .......
34. $9 \times 5 =$ .......
35. $8 \times 8 =$ .......
36. $9 \times 7 =$ .......
37. $5 \times 5 =$ .......
38. $6 \times 6 =$ .......
39. $7 \times 5 =$ .......
40. $3 \times 9 =$ .......
41. $8 \times 5 =$ .......
42. $8 \times 8 =$ .......
43. $9 \times 8 =$ .......
44. $4 \times 7 =$ .......
45. $5 \times 7 =$ .......
46. $7 \times 7 =$ .......
47. $6 \times 9 =$ .......
48. $9 \times 9 =$ .......

# Reading a Plan

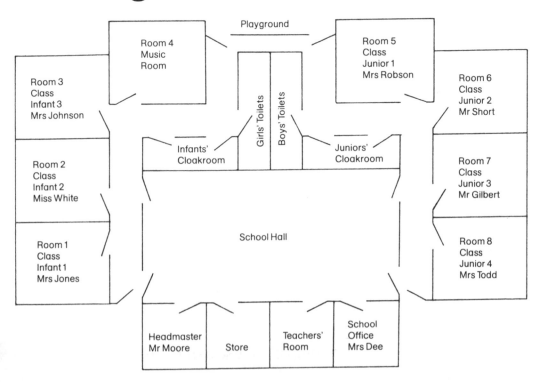

Look carefully at this plan and then answer these questions.

1. This school has .......... class-rooms.

2. There are .......... class-rooms for infants.

3. There are .......... class-rooms for juniors.

4. A special room is for ................................

5. The room next to the school office is the ................................

6. The room next to the Headmaster's room is the ................................

7. The school hall has .......... doors.

8. The school has .......... entrances.

9. Class Junior 2 is taught by ................................ in Room ..........

10. Class Infant 3 is taught by ................................ in Room ..........

11. On the way from Mrs Robson's class-room to Mrs Todd's
    class-room I would pass ................................................................

12. If Mrs Jones went from her class-room to the music room, on the way she would
    pass ................................................................

13. On the way from Class Infant 1 to the playground a child would pass ....................
    ................................................................

14. From the teachers' room to the music room the shortest way is ........................
    ................................................................

# Measuring Lines

_____ cm _____ U

_____ cm _____ V

_____ cm _____ W

_____ cm _____ X

_____ cm _____ Y

_____ cm _____ Z

Above each line, write its length. Then complete these sentences.

1. In order of length from the shortest to the longest,
   the lines are ..................................
2. Line Y is .......cm shorter than Line U.
3. Line X is .......cm longer than Line V.
4. Line U is .......cm shorter than Line X.
5. Line V is .......cm longer than Line Y.
6. Line W is .......cm shorter than Line Y.
7. Line Z is .......cm longer than Line U.
8. Line W is half the length of Line ........
9. Line V is twice the length of Line ........
10. Three lines like W would equal the length of Line ........
11. Line X is four times the length of Line ........
12. Lines W and Z together equal the length of Line ........
13. Lines U and Y are together 1cm longer than Line ........
14. Lines W and Z are together 1cm longer than Lines ....... and .......
    together.
15. By how much are all the lines together more than
    half a metre? .......

# Plurals

Write new words to make **plurals** of these, like this:

bear **bears**          dress **dresses**          foot **feet**

| | Word | Plural | | | Word | Plural |
|---|---|---|---|---|---|---|
| 1. | apple | ................... | | 26. | face | ................... |
| 2. | orange | ................... | | 27. | family | ................... |
| 3. | office | ................... | | 28. | party | ................... |
| 4. | bicycle | ................... | | 29. | fly | ................... |
| 5. | penny | ................... | | 30. | bird | ................... |
| 6. | game | ................... | | 31. | postman | ................... |
| 7. | body | ................... | | 32. | girl | ................... |
| 8. | queen | ................... | | 33. | box | ................... |
| 9. | holiday | ................... | | 34. | rabbit | ................... |
| 10. | boy | ................... | | 35. | horse | ................... |
| 11. | room | ................... | | 36. | bus | ................... |
| 12. | insect | ................... | | 37. | sheep | ................... |
| 13. | cake | ................... | | 38. | infant | ................... |
| 14. | story | ................... | | 39. | church | ................... |
| 15. | jelly | ................... | | 40. | tooth | ................... |
| 16. | class | ................... | | 41. | job | ................... |
| 17. | toy | ................... | | 42. | coat | ................... |
| 18. | child | ................... | | 43. | knife | ................... |
| 19. | uncle | ................... | | 44. | cry | ................... |
| 20. | kennel | ................... | | 45. | woman | ................... |
| 21. | daisy | ................... | | 46. | lady | ................... |
| 22. | day | ................... | | 47. | lunch | ................... |
| 23. | dish | ................... | | 48. | man | ................... |
| 24. | mother | ................... | | 49. | nest | ................... |
| 25. | eye | ................... | | 50. | noise | ................... |

# Factors

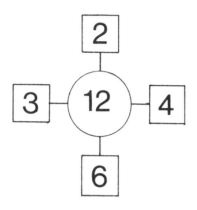

Look at this drawing.
It shows **2** in the top box and **6** in the bottom box.
**2 × 6 = 12**, so **12** goes in the circle for the answer.
But **12** can also be made from the factors **3** and **4**.
**3 × 4 = 12**, so **12** is the answer again.
The number **12** has **four** factors: **2, 3, 4** and **6**.
So the number **12** must have **four** boxes round
its circle.

Now try these. Put the correct answer in each circle.
Remember that the number you put in the circle must be the answer
to **both** pairs of factors.

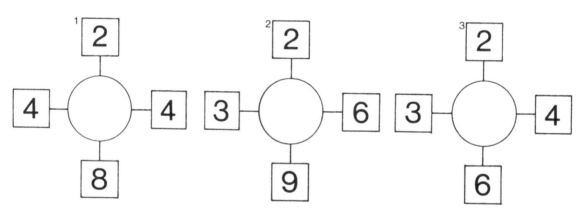

These are the opposite way round. The number has been put in
the circle. You have to find the right pairs of factors and
put them in the boxes.

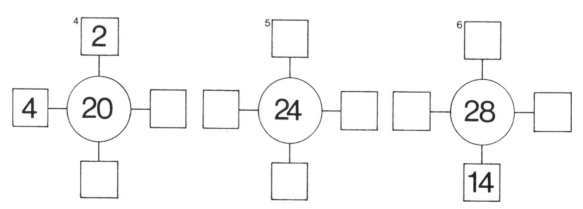

20

# Alphabetical Order

Put the words in each box into alphabetical order.
Look at the first letter in each word. This usually tells you
where it must go in alphabetical order. But if the
first letters of two words are the same, you must look at the
second letters, or even the third letters, to find out the order.
The first one has been started for you.
Here is the alphabet to help you.

**a b c d e f g h i j k l m n o p q r s t u v w x y z**

**1**

| | |
|---|---|
| **above** | **above** |
| add | |
| bread | |
| ball | |

**2**

| | |
|---|---|
| dead | |
| date | |
| cried | |
| clean | |

**3**

| | |
|---|---|
| find | |
| evening | |
| family | |
| end | |

**4**

| | |
|---|---|
| Monday | |
| lorry | |
| little | |
| meet | |

**5**

| | |
|---|---|
| ride | |
| seven | |
| real | |
| stand | |

**6**

| | |
|---|---|
| try | |
| tried | |
| true | |
| track | |

**7**

| | |
|---|---|
| sheep | |
| shall | |
| shoot | |
| ship | |

**8**

| | |
|---|---|
| sting | |
| stand | |
| steal | |
| straight | |

# Class Attendances

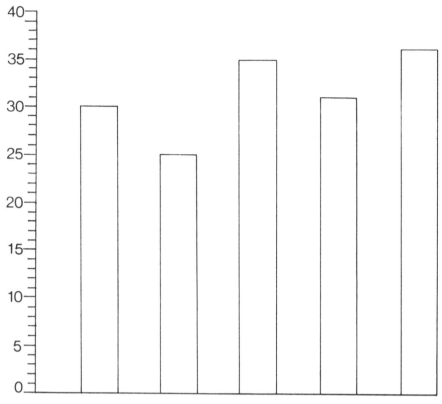

Monday   Tuesday  Wednesday  Thursday  Friday

This is a bar graph.
It shows the number of children who were present
on each day of the school week.
There are 36 children in this class.
Look at the graph carefully and complete the sentences below.

1. There were .......... children present on Monday.

2. There were .......... children present on Tuesday.

3. There were .......... children present on Wednesday.

4. There were .......... children present on Thursday.

5. There were .......... children present on Friday.

6. The day that most children were absent was ...........

7. The day no children were absent was ...........

8. There were .......... children absent on Monday.

9. There were .......... children absent on Wednesday.

10. There were .......... children absent on Thursday.

11. During the week the class had a total of ......... absences.

12. On ......... days of the week there were more than 30 children present.

# Name the Birds

Write the correct name neatly in the space below each bird.
Colour each bird to make a small picture.
Here are the names to help you.
They are not in the right order.

**pelican**     **gull**     **vulture**     **ostrich**     **wren**     **puffin**

**swan**     **woodpecker**     **eagle**     **stork**     **penguin**     **pigeon**

# The Magic Division Square

| | 1 | 2 | 3 | 4 | 5 | 6 | 7 | 8 | 9 |
|---|---|---|---|---|---|---|---|---|---|
| 1 | 1 | 2 | 3 | 4 | 5 | 6 | 7 | 8 | 9 |
| 2 | 2 | 4 | 6 | 8 | 10 | 12 | 14 | 16 | 18 |
| 3 | 3 | 6 | 9 | 12 | 15 | 18 | 21 | 24 | 27 |
| 4 | 4 | 8 | 12 | 16 | 20 | 24 | 28 | 32 | 36 |
| 5 | 5 | 10 | 15 | 20 | 25 | 30 | 35 | 40 | 45 |
| 6 | 6 | 12 | 18 | 24 | 30 | 36 | 42 | 48 | 54 |
| 7 | 7 | 14 | 21 | 28 | 35 | 42 | 49 | 56 | 63 |
| 8 | 8 | 16 | 24 | 32 | 40 | 48 | 56 | 64 | 72 |
| 9 | 9 | 18 | 27 | 36 | 45 | 54 | 63 | 72 | 81 |

If you want to use it to work out **54 ÷ 9**:
Put your finger on **9** in the top line.
Move your finger downwards until it is on **54**.
The answer is the figure at the far left, which is **6**.

Now try these, using the **magic division square**.

1. $12 \div 6 = $.......
2. $14 \div 2 = $.......
3. $21 \div 7 = $.......
4. $24 \div 3 = $.......
5. $32 \div 8 = $.......
6. $56 \div 8 = $.......
7. $54 \div 6 = $.......
8. $21 \div 7 = $.......
9. $48 \div 8 = $.......
10. $18 \div 9 = $.......
11. $24 \div 8 = $.......
12. $56 \div 7 = $.......
13. $15 \div 5 = $.......
14. $18 \div 3 = $.......
15. $28 \div 4 = $.......
16. $18 \div 2 = $.......

17. $36 \div 4 = $.......
18. $45 \div 9 = $.......
19. $81 \div 9 = $.......
20. $36 \div 9 = $.......
21. $16 \div 2 = $.......
22. $32 \div 4 = $.......
23. $42 \div 6 = $.......
24. $72 \div 9 = $.......
25. $24 \div 4 = $.......
26. $30 \div 6 = $.......
27. $16 \div 8 = $.......
28. $42 \div 7 = $.......
29. $49 \div 7 = $.......
30. $48 \div 6 = $.......
31. $63 \div 9 = $.......
32. $40 \div 8 = $.......

33. $27 \div 3 = $.......
34. $45 \div 5 = $.......
35. $64 \div 8 = $.......
36. $63 \div 7 = $.......
37. $25 \div 5 = $.......
38. $36 \div 6 = $.......
39. $35 \div 5 = $.......
40. $27 \div 9 = $.......
41. $40 \div 5 = $.......
42. $64 \div 8 = $.......
43. $72 \div 9 = $.......
44. $28 \div 7 = $.......
45. $35 \div 7 = $.......
46. $49 \div 7 = $.......
47. $54 \div 9 = $.......
48. $81 \div 9 = $.......

# A Calendar for Two Months

Look at the calendar carefully. Then complete the sentences.

MAY

| Sunday | | 6 | 13 | 20 | 27 |
|---|---|---|---|---|---|
| Monday | | 7 | 14 | 21 | 28 |
| Tuesday | 1 | 8 | 15 | 22 | 29 |
| Wednesday | 2 | 9 | 16 | 23 | 30 |
| Thursday | 3 | 10 | 17 | 24 | 31 |
| Friday | 4 | 11 | 18 | 25 | |
| Saturday | 5 | 12 | 19 | 26 | |

JUNE

| Sunday | | 3 | 10 | 17 | 24 |
|---|---|---|---|---|---|
| Monday | | 4 | 11 | 18 | 25 |
| Tuesday | | 5 | 12 | 19 | 26 |
| Wednesday | | 6 | 13 | 20 | 27 |
| Thursday | | 7 | 14 | 21 | 28 |
| Friday | 1 | 8 | 15 | 22 | 29 |
| Saturday | 2 | 9 | 16 | 23 | 30 |

1. The first day of May is a ..............................
2. The first day of June is a ..............................
3. The last day of May is a ..............................
4. The last day of June is a ..............................
5. There are ....... days in May.
6. There are ....... days in June.
7. There are ....... Wednesdays in May.
8. There are ....... Mondays in June.
9. From 8th to 22nd May there are ....... days.
10. From 29th May to 5th June there are ....... days.
11. The 23rd May is a ..............................
    The 23rd June is a ..............................
12. The date of the fourth Tuesday in May is the ........
13. The date of the fifth Friday in June is the ........
14. From 2nd May to 27th June there are ....... weeks.
15. The first day of the next month (July) will be a ..............................

# Areas of Rectangles

1. This rectangle is **2** cm wide and has **2** rows of centimetre squares.
It is **3** cm long and has **3** centimetre squares in each row.
It contains **6** centimetre squares so we say that its **area** is **6** centimetre squares.

   Now find the measurements and the areas of these other rectangles.

2. This rectangle is ....... cm wide and has ....... rows of centimetre squares.
It is ....... cm long and has ....... centimetre squares in each row.
It contains ....... centimetre squares so we say that its area is ....... centimetre squares.

3. This rectangle is ....... cm wide and has ....... rows of centimetre squares.
It is ....... cm long and has ....... centimetre squares in each row.
It contains ....... centimetre squares so we say that its area is ....... centimetre squares.

4. This rectangle is ....... cm wide and has ....... rows of centimetre squares.
It is ....... cm long and has ....... centimetre squares in each row.
It contains ....... centimetre squares so we say that its area is ....... centimetre squares.

5. This rectangle is ....... cm wide and has ....... rows of centimetre squares.
It is ....... cm long and has ....... centimetre squares in each row.
It contains ....... centimetre squares so we say that its area is ....... centimetre squares.

26

# Words Instead of Phrases

1. John came downstairs and had his <u>first meal of the day</u>.

2. Mother took Tracy to the <u>man who makes people better</u>.

3. Dad painted the <u>wooden wall</u> round the garden on his day off.

4. We all went to visit Grandma at the <u>place where sick people are looked after</u>.

5. We found some <u>small creatures with six legs each</u> in the woods.

6. Mother cleaned out the <u>room where the food is cooked</u>.

7. After tea Dad took us all to the <u>building where books are kept</u>.

8. In her hand Diane had her <u>small bag for carrying money</u>.

9. Every morning we walk to <u>the place where children are taught</u>.

10. In the <u>time of the year after spring</u> we go to Wales on holiday.

11. When the weather is hot I wear <u>shoes that are held on by straps</u>.

12. On our way home we became wet because of the <u>drops of water that fall from the clouds</u>.

Write these sentences again, using **one word** instead of the groups of words which have a line under them.
The first one has been done for you.

1. John came downstairs and had his **breakfast**.

2. ...................................................................................................

3. ...................................................................................................

4. ...................................................................................................

5. ...................................................................................................

6. ...................................................................................................

7. ...................................................................................................

8. ...................................................................................................

9. ...................................................................................................

10. ...................................................................................................

11. ...................................................................................................

12. ...................................................................................................

# Operating Numbers

Do what it says to the numbers in the circles.
Put your answers in the squares.

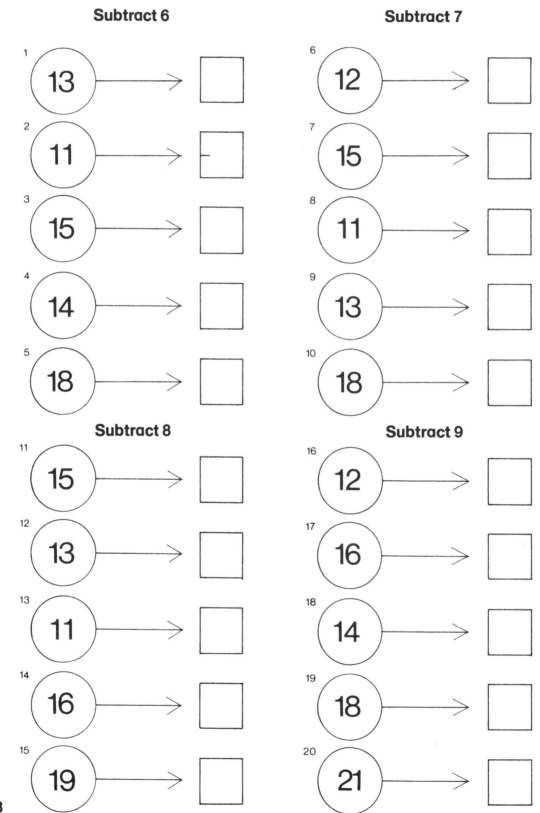

**Subtract 6**

1   ( 13 ) → ☐

2   ( 11 ) → ☐

3   ( 15 ) → ☐

4   ( 14 ) → ☐

5   ( 18 ) → ☐

**Subtract 7**

6   ( 12 ) → ☐

7   ( 15 ) → ☐

8   ( 11 ) → ☐

9   ( 13 ) → ☐

10   ( 18 ) → ☐

**Subtract 8**

11   ( 15 ) → ☐

12   ( 13 ) → ☐

13   ( 11 ) → ☐

14   ( 16 ) → ☐

15   ( 19 ) → ☐

**Subtract 9**

16   ( 12 ) → ☐

17   ( 16 ) → ☐

18   ( 14 ) → ☐

19   ( 18 ) → ☐

20   ( 21 ) → ☐

# Map Reading

Here is a map of a village.
The map is divided into six squares, so that you can "read" it.

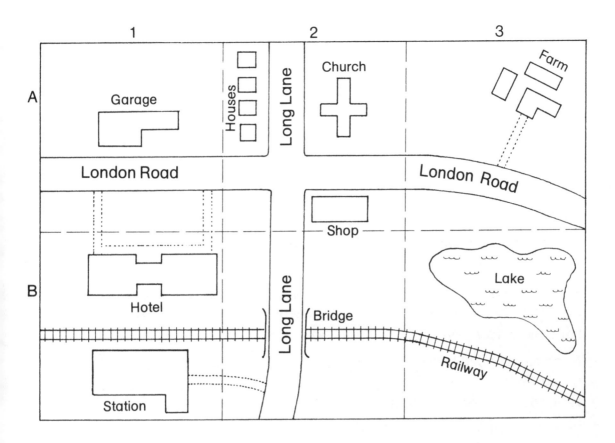

Now complete these sentences. The first one has been done for you.

1.  The crossroads of the village are in square **A2**.
2.  The farm is in square ..........
3.  The garage is in square ..........
4.  The bridge is in square ..........
5.  The lake is in square ..........
6.  The church is in square ..........
7.  The hotel is in square ..........
8.  The shop is in square ..........
9.  The station is in square ..........
10. London Road goes through squares .............................
11. The railway goes through squares .............................
12. Long Lane goes through squares .............................
13. The houses are in square ..........
14. To get from the farm to the lake you must cross .............................
15. To get from the station to the garage you must go .............................
    .............................

# How Many Hours?

Find the answers to these questions.

Use this clock to help you to count
the number of hours each time.

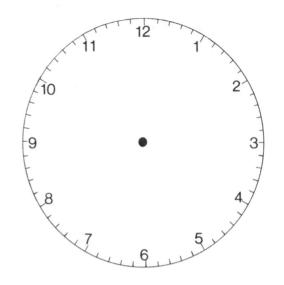

1. Morning school lasts from 9 o'clock until 12 o'clock.
   That is .......... hours.

2. Afternoon school lasts from half past 1 until half past 3.
   That is .......... hours.

3. Every day I leave home at 8 o'clock in the morning and I get
   home from school at 4 o'clock in the afternoon.
   I am away from home .......... hours each day.

4. Each night I go to bed at 8 o'clock. Each morning I get up
   at 7 o'clock.
   I spend .......... hours in bed.

5. The film I watched on television last night lasted from half
   past 4 until 6 o'clock.
   It lasted .......... hours.

6. Mother went out shopping at half past 9 and returned home at
   12 o'clock.
   She spent .......... hours shopping.

7. Daddy went to work at 8 o'clock in the morning and got back
   from work at half past 6 in the evening.
   He was away at work for .......... hours.

8. On Saturday my friends came to play at half past 2 in the
   afternoon. They went home at 6 o'clock.
   They played with me for .......... hours.

9. When Grandma comes to look after us, Mum and Dad go out at
   half past 6 in the evening and come back at 11 o'clock.
   They go out for .......... hours.

10. When Mum and Dad took us to the seaside for a day we started
    out at half past 7 in the morning. We didn't get home until
    10 o'clock at night.
    Our day out lasted .......... hours.

# True or False

Read these sentences carefully. Some are true and some are false.
Write out the true ones on the lines below.

1. A school is a place where children are educated.
2. A liner is a kind of large ocean-going ship.
3. A tape-recorder is used for listening to the radio.
4. A calendar is used for telling the time during the day.
5. A Dalmatian is a white dog with black spots.
6. The month of May is the sixth month of the year.
7. An owl is a bird that flies mostly at night.
8. Most triangles have four sides.
9. A dictionary is used for learning the meanings of words and how to spell them.
10. A crocodile is a reptile and lays eggs.
11. The word bicycle means something which has two wheels.
12. Squirrels live mainly in burrows in the ground.
13. Roast beef is meat that has been cooked by boiling it.
14. There are twenty-four letters in the alphabet.
15. The middle light of traffic-lights is yellow and means "take care".

These are true sentences:

..... .................................................................................................................

..... .................................................................................................................

..... .................................................................................................................

..... .................................................................................................................

..... .................................................................................................................

..... .................................................................................................................

..... .................................................................................................................

# Magic Squares

Fill in the missing numbers so that each row of three numbers (down, across or diagonal) adds to the same amount.

**1**

|   |    |   |
|---|----|---|
|   |    |   |
|   |    | 2 |
| 1 | 12 | 5 |

**2**

| 10 | 1 | 7 |
|----|---|---|
| 3  |   |   |
|    |   |   |

**3**

| 9 |   | 8 |
|---|---|---|
|   | 6 |   |
| 4 |   |   |

**4**

|   | 2  |   |
|---|----|---|
|   | 6  |   |
|   | 10 | 5 |

**5**

| 5 |   |   |
|---|---|---|
| 4 |   |   |
| 9 | 2 |   |

**6**

| 9 |   |    |
|---|---|----|
|   | 6 | 10 |
|   |   | 3  |